Overview *Puppets*

Explore the world of puppets and the people who make them move.

Reading Vocabulary Words

stage *screen*
puppeteers

High-Frequency Words

hands	*finger*
move	*hide*
pulls	*move*
pen	*their*

Building Future Vocabulary

* These vocabulary words do not appear in this text. They are provided to develop related oral vocabulary that first appears in future texts.

Words:	*manage*	*curious*	*prop*
Levels:	Gold	Library	Library

Comprehension Strategy
Using decoding skills

Fluency Skill
Accurately pronouncing difficult words

Phonics Skill
Identifying and segmenting syllables in spoken words (puppeteers, television)

Reading-Writing Connection
Labeling a diagram

Home Connection
Send home one of the Flying Colors Take-Home books for children to share with their families.

Differentiated Instruction
Before reading the text, query children to discover their level of understanding of the comprehension strategy — Using decoding skills. As you work together, provide additional support to children who show a beginning mastery of the strategy.

Focus on ELL
- Look through the book with children to determine which kinds of puppets they are familiar with. Have children describe a puppet they have seen in person or on television.

- Have children draw a picture of the puppet.

T1

Using This Teaching Version

1 Before Reading

1. Before Reading

2. During Reading

3. Revisiting the Text

4. Assessment

This Teaching Version will assist you in directing children through the process of reading.

1. **Begin with Before Reading** to familiarize children with the book's content. Select the skills and strategies that meet the needs of your children.

2. **Next, go to During Reading** to help children become familiar with the text, and then to read individually on their own.

3. **Then, go back to Revisiting the Text** and select those specific activities that meet children's needs.

4. **Finally, finish with Assessment** to confirm children are ready to move forward to the next text.

Building Background

- Write the word *puppeteers* on the board. Explain that puppeteers are the people who make puppets move. Have children clap the syllables for *puppeteers* as they repeat the word after you. Have children share what they know about puppeteers and puppet shows. Correct any misinformation.

- Introduce the book by reading the title, talking about the cover photograph, and sharing the overview.

Building Future Vocabulary
Use Interactive Modeling Card: Word Log

- Write the words *manage*, *curious*, and *prop* in the first column of the Word Log.

- Tell children you will complete the Word Log together after they read the book.

Introduction to Reading Vocabulary

- On blank cards write: *stage*, *puppeteers*, and *screen*. Read them aloud. Tell children these words will appear in the text of *Puppets*.

- Use each word in a sentence for understanding.

Introduction to Comprehension Strategy

Use Interactive Modeling Card: Nonfiction Questions and Answers

- Explain that decoding skills help us to recognize words as we read. Say *You already know many words from hearing and using them. Now you are learning what those words look like in a text.* Explain to children that they will use decoding skills as they read *Puppets*.

- Introduce the Nonfiction Questions and Answers chart. Ask children what they know about puppets; list the responses in the first column. Discuss what children would like to learn from reading *Puppets;* list their questions in the second column. Tell children to keep these questions in mind as they read *Puppets*.

Introduction to Phonics

- Say **television**. With children, clap the syllables as they repeat the word. Then say each syllable separately, pausing after each one. Have children repeat the sounds.

- Together brainstorm other words that begin with the same first syllables as **television**. (**telephone, telescope**)

Modeling Fluency

- Have children read aloud page 13 with you. Ask *Which word is hard to read and say? (fabric)*

- Explain that pronouncing difficult words accurately helps readers understand what they are reading.

2 During Reading

Book Talk

Beginning on page T4, use the During Reading notes on the left-hand side to engage children in a book talk. On page 24, follow with Individual Reading.

During Reading

Book Talk
- Discuss how to use a table of contents. Ask *Where in the book would you look to find out how to make a puppet?* (Chapter 9, page 23)
- Remind children to add questions to the Nonfiction Questions and Answers chart as they think of them.

Turn to page 2 — Book Talk

Puppets

Julie Haydon

Contents

Chapter 1	In a Play	2
Chapter 2	Making Puppets Move	4
Chapter 3	About Puppets	8
Chapter 4	Finger Puppets	11
Chapter 5	Hand Puppets	13
Chapter 6	Stick Puppets	16
Chapter 7	String Puppets	18
Chapter 8	Shadow Puppets	20
Chapter 9	Make a Puppet	23
Glossary and Index		24

Revisiting the Text

Future Vocabulary
- Display the Word Log you started earlier in the lesson and point to the word *curious*. Ask *What does* curious *mean?* Have volunteers suggest meanings for *curious* and write these in the second column of the Word Log.

Now revisit pages 2–3

During Reading

Book Talk

- **Comprehension Strategy**
  Ask *What are actors?* (people in a play) Direct children to look at the photographs on pages 2–3. Ask *Which picture shows actors?* (the one on page 2) *What does the picture on page 3 show?* (puppets) Discuss how using picture clues can help children decode words—or discover what they mean—as they read.

- Introduce the word *stage*. Say *A stage is the raised area in a theater or auditorium. The stage is raised so people in the audience can see what is happening on it.* Have children locate the word *stage* on pages 2–3.

Turn to page 4 – Book Talk

Revisiting the Text

This is a puppet play.
There are no people in this play.
The puppets are on a stage, too.

Future Vocabulary
- Point to *prop* on the Word Log. Say *Look at the swords the actors are holding. The sword is a prop. A prop is something an actor uses onstage.* Write this meaning of *prop* in the second column of the Word Log.

Now revisit pages 4–5

During Reading

Book Talk

- **Phonics Skill** Read page 4 aloud. Say *Puppeteer* *is a long word. Let's clap and count the syllables together.*

- **Comprehension Strategy** Have children locate the word *puppeteers* on page 4. Ask *What word can you find inside puppeteers? (puppet)* Discuss how looking for smaller words inside long words can help us understand what we read.

Turn to page 6 – Book Talk

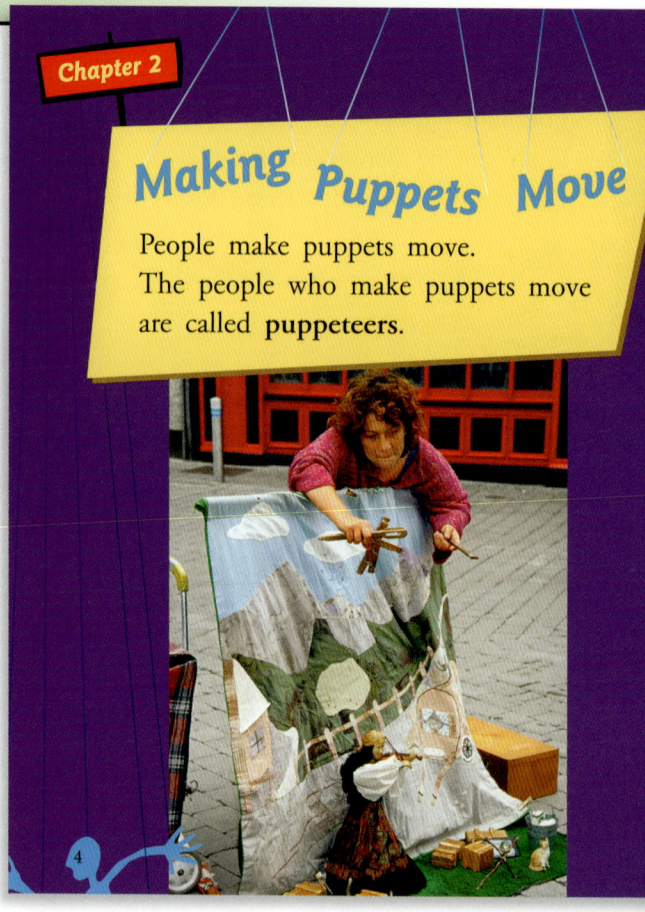

Revisiting the Text

Puppeteers move their puppets around on the stage. Some puppeteers do the voices for their puppets, too.

Future Vocabulary

- Direct children's attention to the picture on page 4. Have children point to the props in the picture. (the small items on the green mat) Ask *Can you find a prop in the picture on page 5?* (the ball in the puppet's hand, the crutch, the backpack on the stage) Have children use *prop* in a sentence.

Now revisit pages 6–7

During Reading

Book Talk

- Introduce the word *screen*. Point to the *screen* in the photograph on page 7 and say *This is a screen. The puppeteer is behind the screen. The audience is in front of the screen. The audience sees the shadows of the puppets.*

- Say *We look at many different kinds of screens. We watch movies on a screen. We look at a screen when we use a computer. What else do you watch on a screen?* (television shows) Have children use the word *screen* in a sentence.

Turn to page 8 — Book Talk

Sometimes puppeteers stand on the stage with their puppets.
The puppeteers wear black clothes so they are hard to see.

Revisiting the Text

Sometimes puppeteers hide behind the stage.

Future Vocabulary

- Display the Word Log and point to the word *manage*. Say *Manage means to keep control or handle something properly. People can manage things or other people. Puppeteers manage their puppets.*

- Ask *What does it mean to say someone manages to do something?* (They do something properly.) *What does it mean to say someone manages a department of ten people?* (That person is in charge of ten people.) *What does it mean to manage your money well?* (You save and spend your money wisely.) With children, fill in the second column of the Word Log for *manage*.

Now revisit pages 8–9

During Reading

Book Talk

- Point out and read aloud the captions on page 8. Say *These words are captions. What do captions tell us?* (They tell us about the pictures.) *Which caption goes with which picture?*

- **Phonics Skill** Read page 9 aloud. Have children locate the word *television* on the page. Say Television *is a long word. Let's clap and count the syllables together.*

- **Comprehension Strategy** Write *television* on the board and underline *-vision*. Ask *What does* vision *mean?* (sight, seeing) Compare the words *television* and *telephone*. Ask *How are these two words alike?* (Both begin with *tele*.) *How are they different?* (They have different endings and different meanings.) Discuss the meanings of the parts of these words. (*Tele* means "long distance," *phone* means "sound," and *vision* means "see.")

Turn to page 10 — Book Talk

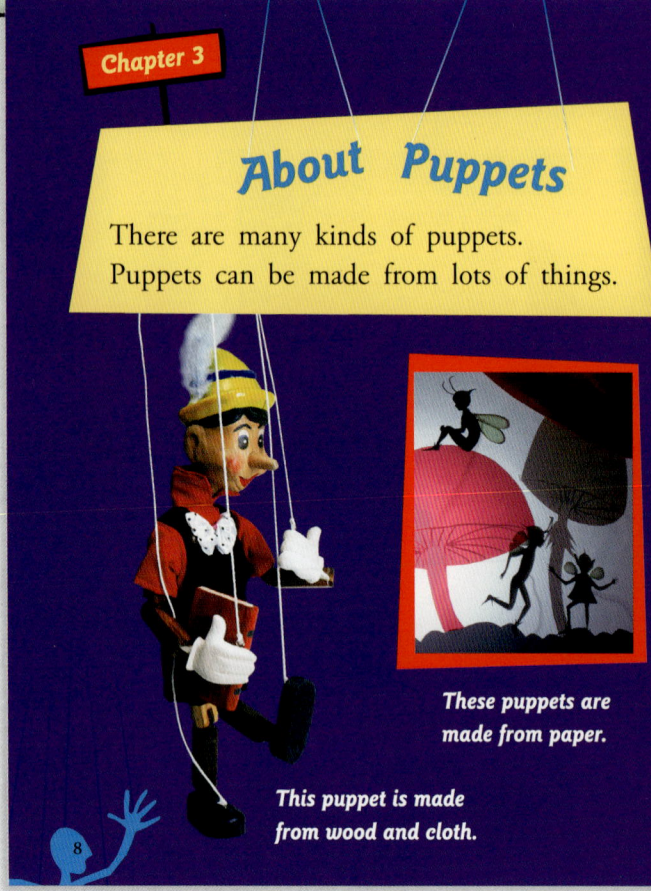

8

Revisiting the Text

You can see puppets in plays, on television, and in movies.

Future Vocabulary

- Ask children if they are curious about the puppet on page 9. Ask *What do you wonder about this puppet?* (Was the puppet in a movie? What kind of animal is the puppet?) *What else are you curious about?* Have children complete the sentence stem *I am curious about ____.*

- Explain that being curious is a good way to learn about new things, but it can also be dangerous. Discuss general safety rules and what children should and should not do when they are curious about something new.

↪ **Now revisit pages 10–11**

During Reading

Book Talk

- Say *Look at the puppet on page 11. What do we call this kind of puppet?* (a finger puppet) *Why?* (because it fits over a finger)

- Have children pretend that they have a finger puppet and act out how they would make the puppet move. Say *You are all* puppeteers. *You are making your finger puppet move.* Have children use *puppeteer* in a sentence describing themselves or their classmates and their finger puppets.

➡ *Turn to page 12 – Book Talk*

Puppets can look like people, animals, monsters, or other things.

10

Revisiting the Text

Future Vocabulary
- Ask *Which of the puppets are easiest to manage?* (finger puppets) Have children explain why some puppets are easier or harder to use. Instruct them to use the word *manage* in their responses.

Now revisit pages 12–13

During Reading

Book Talk

- Have a volunteer read the text on page 13. Then compare and contrast finger puppets and hand puppets. Ask *How are finger puppets and hand puppets alike?* (They are both puppets; they both fit over a part of your body.) *How are they different?* (Hand puppets are bigger.)

Turn to page 14 – Book Talk

Sometimes fingers can be made *into* puppets. These finger puppets were made with a pen.

Revisiting the Text

Chapter 5

Hand Puppets

A hand puppet fits over a hand.

These hand puppets have heads and hands.

Their bodies are made from fabric.

Future Vocabulary

- Ask *Do you see any props on this page?* (Yes, a teddy bear.) Discuss alternate meanings for *prop*. Say *If something is falling down, you can prop it up with something strong. What would you use to prop up a tent?* (a pole or stick) Have children use *prop* in a sentence about something falling down. Add this meaning for *prop* to the Word Log.

Now revisit pages 14–15

During Reading

Book Talk

- **Comprehension Strategy**
  Have children locate *puppeteers* on page 15. Say *We already noticed that* puppeteers *includes the word* puppet. *Now let's look at how* puppeteer *ends.* Write *puppeteer* on the board and underline *-teer*. Ask *What other words end in* -teer? *(volunteer, musketeer) What do all the words have in common?* (They all refer to people.) Discuss how knowing what word parts mean can help us decode unfamiliar words.

Turn to page 16 – Book Talk

The puppeteers wear the puppets on their hands.
They move their hands and fingers to make the puppets move.

14

Revisiting the Text

This hand puppet has a mouth that moves. The puppeteer opens and shuts his hand to make the mouth move.

Future Vocabulary
- Ask *How many puppeteers does it take to manage a hand puppet?* (one) Explain that some puppets are so big with so many moving parts that it may take two or even three puppeteers to manage them.

Now revisit pages 16–17

During Reading

Book Talk

- Compare and contrast stick puppets with hand and finger puppets. Ask *How are stick puppets like hand and finger puppets?* (They are all puppets; they all move.) *How are they different?* (Stick puppets are on a stick; stick puppets do not fit over a part of your body.)

- Remind children that they can add questions to the Nonfiction Questions and Answers chart.

Turn to page 18 – Book Talk

Chapter 6

Stick Puppets

A stick puppet has a stick inside it. Sometimes the puppet's head is at the end of the stick.

The puppeteer holds onto the stick with one hand.

Revisiting the Text

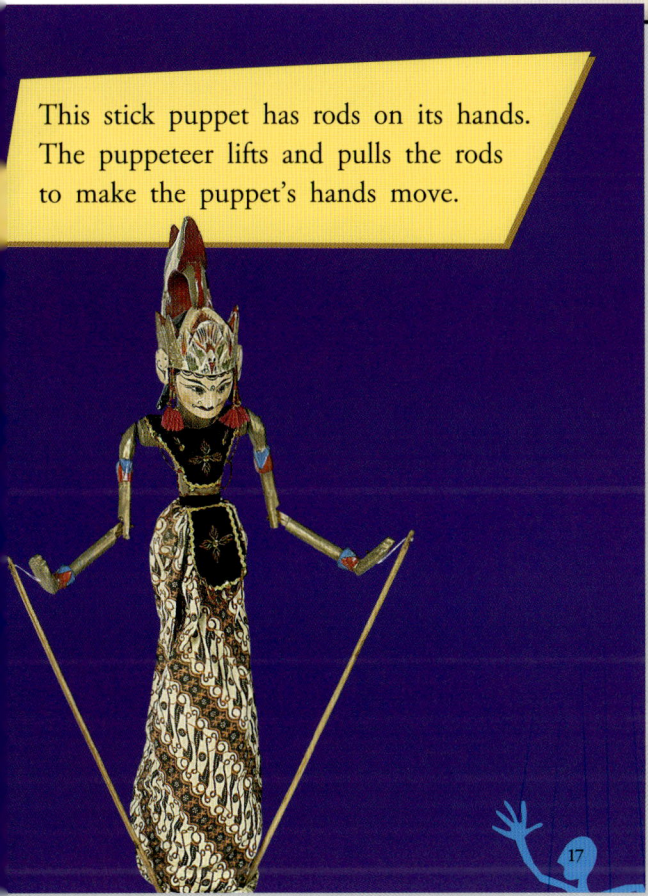

This stick puppet has rods on its hands. The puppeteer lifts and pulls the rods to make the puppet's hands move.

Future Vocabulary
- Compare and contrast the stick puppets on pages 16 and 17. Ask *Which one would be easier to manage?* (the stick puppet on page 16) *Why?* (It doesn't have rods.)

Now revisit pages 18–19

During Reading

Book Talk

- Compare and contrast string puppets with the other kinds of puppets children already saw in *Puppets.* Ask *If you could have only one kind of puppet, which would you choose?* Have children explain their answers.

- **Phonics Skill** Say *Another name for a string puppet is* marionette. Have children repeat the word and clap out the syllables.

Turn to page 20 — Book Talk

Revisiting the Text

The puppeteer can make the sticks and the strings go up and down and to the side.
This moves the puppet.

Future Vocabulary

- Say *Look at the people watching the puppeteer in the photograph on page 19. Do you think they are* curious? *Are you* curious *about puppets and puppeteers?* Discuss how people ask questions when they are curious. Ask *What questions would you ask a puppeteer?* (When did you start being a puppeteer? What was your first puppet? Do you make your own puppets?)

Now revisit pages 20–21

During Reading

Book Talk

- Ask *When do you see your shadow on the ground outside?* (when the sun is out; on a sunny day) Talk about shadows and light so children better understand what they see in the photographs on pages 20–21.

- Make sure that children understand that the *puppeteer* works behind the *screen* and the audience sits in front of the *screen*. Have children use *screen* in a sentence that describes one of the pictures on these pages.

➡ *Turn to page 22 – Book Talk*

Revisiting the Text

A shadow puppet is held behind a **screen**. When a light shines on the puppet, its shadow falls on the screen.

Future Vocabulary
- Ask *Are you curious about the puppeteer in this picture? What questions would you ask him?* (Why do you like shadow puppets? What is the shadow play about? What country are you from?)

Now revisit pages 22–23

During Reading

Book Talk
- Leave this page spread for children to discover on their own when they read the book individually.

➡ Turn to page 24 – Book Talk

People sit in front of the screen to watch the puppet play.

Revisiting the Text

Chapter 9

Make a Puppet

You will need:
- a small paper plate
- paints or felt pens
- a straw
- glue

1. Paint a face and some hair on your paper plate. Let it dry.
2. Glue the straw to the back of the plate.

Future Vocabulary

- Point out that the directions on page 23 have bullets and numbers to make them easier to follow. Explain that the small squares are called bullets. Discuss when bullets are used in texts (for lists). Say *Bullets can make a list easier to manage.*

- Ask *Why are there numbers in front of the last two paragraphs?* Discuss how numbers in texts are used to show the order of steps. Show children examples of bullets and numbered lists in other texts, if available.

Go to page T5 — Revisiting the Text

23

During Reading

Book Talk
* Note: Point out this text feature page as a reference point for children's usage while reading independently.

Individual Reading
Have each child read the entire book at his or her own pace while remaining in the group.

Go to page T5 – Revisiting the Text

Glossary

actors	people who act out a story in a play
play	a story told by actors on a stage
puppeteers	people who make puppets move around
screen	thin paper or cloth that you look at to watch a shadow puppet play

Index

actors   2
play   2, 3, 9, 22
puppeteers   4, 5, 6, 7, 14, 15, 16, 17, 18, 19, 20
screen   21, 22
stage   2, 3, 5, 6, 7
voices   5

24

During independent work time, children can read the online book at:
www.rigbyflyingcolors.com

24

Revisiting the Text

Future Vocabulary
- Use the notes on the right-hand pages to develop oral vocabulary that goes beyond the text. These vocabulary words first appear in future texts. These words are: *manage*, *curious*, and *prop*.

Turn back to page 1

Reading Vocabulary Review
Activity Sheet: Word Web

- Have children write the words *stage*, *puppeteers*, and *screen* in the outer boxes of the Word Web. Ask volunteers to explain how they are alike. (They are all found at puppet shows.)
- Have children write *puppet show* in the circle. Have children fill in the remaining spaces with other things they might see at a puppet show.

Comprehension Strategy Review
Use Interactive Modeling Card: Nonfiction Questions and Answers

- Discuss *Puppets*. Review the questions children had before they read *Puppets*.
- With children, fill in the rest of the Nonfiction Question and Answers chart.

Phonics Review
- Have children clap the syllables of *puppeteers* and *television* as they say each word together.
- Have children suggest other long words to clap. If children have trouble coming up with words, suggest they use names of characters from their favorite books and movies.

Fluency Review
- Partner children and have them take turns reading each page of the book. Remind them to pronounce difficult words accurately.
- The child who is not reading should follow along to make sure the reader pronounces difficult words accurately.

Reading-Writing Connection
Activity Sheet: Text Connections Web

To assist children with linking reading and writing:

- Model how to use the Text Connections Web. Have children complete the Activity Sheet for *Puppets*.
- Have children draw a picture of a puppet show. Then have them label the parts of their drawing with the words *stage, puppet, puppeteer, screen,* or *prop*.

T5

4 Assessment

Assessing Future Vocabulary

Work with each child individually. Ask questions that elicit each child's understanding of the Future Vocabulary words. Note each child's responses:

- What does a store manager do?
- What do people do when they are curious about something?
- What prop would you use if you were playing a doctor in a play?

Assessing Comprehension Strategy

Work with each child individually. Choose a book the child has not yet read and display a picture from the book. Write several sentences about the picture on the board that contain unfamiliar words that can be decoded using context and picture clues. Have each child read the sentences. Note each child's understanding of using decoding skills:

- Did each child use context and picture clues to decode words?
- Did each child correctly read all the words?
- Was each child able to use decoding skills to recognize the words?

Assessing Phonics

Work with each child individually. Have the child identify and segment syllables in the spoken words *gymnasium, disagreement, unfortunately,* and *predictable.* Note each child's responses for understanding segmenting syllables in spoken words:

- Did each child clap the syllables correctly?
- Did each child pronounce all the syllables correctly?

Assessing Fluency

Have each child read pages 4–5 to you. Note each child's understanding of pronouncing difficult words:

- Was each child able to decode and accurately pronounce all the words?
- Did each child separate the words into syllables?
- Did each child slow down when coming to a difficult word?

Interactive Modeling Cards

Word Log

Title: *Puppets*

Word	Meaning from Selection
manage	handle, direct, be in charge of
curious	nosy, interested
prop	something actors use onstage, hold something up

Directions: With children, fill in the Word Log using the words *manage*, *curious*, and *prop*.

Nonfiction Questions and Answers

Before Reading		During Reading	After Reading
What do I know about this topic?	What do I want to find out by reading this book?	What did I learn?	What new questions do I have?
There are many different kinds of puppets. Puppets move. String puppets are hard to move.	How are puppets made? How do people make puppets move? Where can I learn to move a string puppet?	People in different countries have puppets. Some puppeteers are on the stage with the puppets.	Where can I watch a play with shadow puppets? How can I make a hand puppet? How can I make a string puppet?

Directions: With children, fill in the Nonfiction Questions and Answers chart for *Puppets*.

Discussion Questions

- What kinds of puppets are in this book? (Literal)
- Name a kind of puppet that would be easy to make. (Critical Thinking)
- Why do people put on puppet shows? Why do people watch them? (Inferential)

Activity Sheets

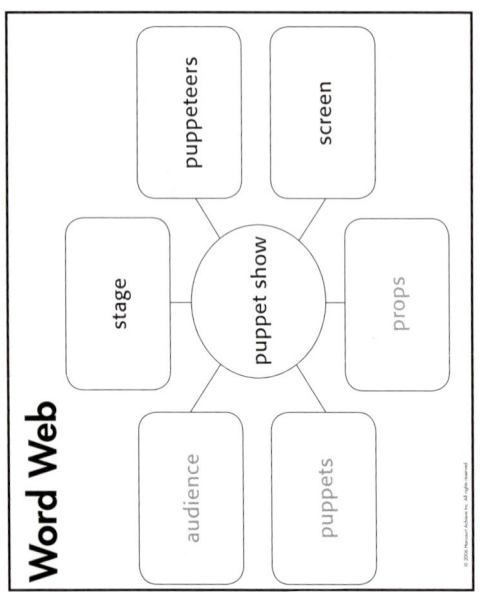

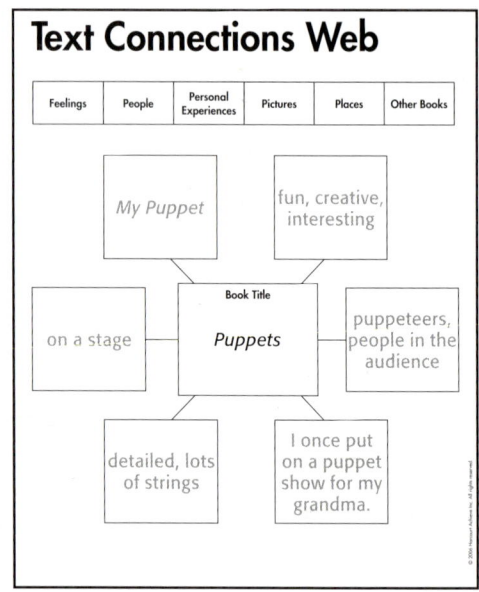

Directions: Have children fill in the Word Web for a puppet show using the words *stage*, *puppeteers*, *screen*, and other things they might see at a puppet show.

Directions: Have children fill in the Text Connections Web for *Puppets*. Optional: On a separate blank paper, have children draw a picture of a puppet show. Then have them label the parts of their drawing with *stage, puppet, puppeteer, screen,* or *prop.*

T8